SCOOBY-DOO!
The Little Book of
SCOOBY-ISMS

PEUK 3080

Published by Ladybird Books Ltd
A Penguin Company
Penguin Books Ltd, 80 Strand, London, WC2R ORL, England
Penguin Books Australia Ltd, Camberwell, Victoria, Australia
Penguin Group (NZ), cnr Airborne and Rosedale Roads, Albany,
Auckland 1310, New Zealand
All rights reserved
2 4 6 8 10 9 7 5 3 1

SCOOBY-DOO!

THE LITTLE BOOK OF SCOOBY-ISMS

An Awesome A-Z of Scooby-Speak!

HEY, DUDES

We're, like, glad you could join us for this
awesome A-Z of Scooby-isms. Now you
too can walk the talk of Mystery Inc. as we revisit
those creepy castles, take a ride in the Mystery
Machine, snaffle a Scooby Snack or two and
generally goof around with Scooby-Doo and the
rest of the super-sleuthing gang.

It's all here: the haunted houses, the creepy capers,
the ghosts and ghouls...

*Zoinks, Scoobs, let's get
outta here!!*

A

All-you-can-eat buffet For eating-machines Scooby and Shaggy, this is their idea of perfect happiness. *See* **Eating-machines**, **Scooby Snacks** and **Shaggy Sandwich**.

Ascot necktie Fred is rarely seen without his distinctive red necktie, a trademark of his clean-cut, good-looking image. *See* **Fred**.

> "Aah-HA... caught red-handed in your foul monster-making schemes with your ugly, evil henchmen!"

Awesome Out of this world. Typical of Shaggy's groovy-speak.

B

Bait Used by the super-sleuthing gang to trap ghostly ghouls and creepy creatures. Usually Scooby and Shaggy end up being the bait. *See* **Red-handed** and **Trap**.

Buddies Scooby and Shaggy are the best of buddies. They share the same hobbies (eating and running away) and have their own secret language. *See* **Scooby Speak** (in appendix).

> SHAGGY
> **"Who's your best buddy?"**
> SCOOBY
> **"Raggy!"**
> SHAGGY
> **"That's right. And who's my best buddy in the whole wide world?"**
> SCOOBY
> **"Rooby-Doo!"**

C

Chilling out Scooby and Shaggy love to do as little as possible, especially after a scary day looking for bad guys.

Clues Crucial to any detective work, the gang are tireless in their search for clues. Footprints often lead to the more obvious clues, while Velma solves the more puzzling ones.

SHAGGY
"Like, chill out, Scooby-Doo, stop shaking!"

SCOOBY
"Re? Rhat's rou!"

SHAGGY
"Oh, right, it is me, sorry."

"Footprints! The Phantom Shadow must have been this way!"

Coolsville Mystery Inc.'s hometown, a place seemingly stuffed full of ghostly ghouls and creepy castles.

D

Daphne (Full name Daphne Blake) Fashion-conscious red-head who likes nothing more than a bit of super-sleuthing with her pals. She also has a nasty habit of being captured by ghouls, hence her nickname, Danger-prone Daphne! *See* **Jeepers!**

"Creepy is my middle name."
SHAGGY

Dark and spooky

Ghostly ghouls or spooky spectres like to hang out in these kind of places – as Scooby and Shaggy know all too well.

FRED
"Look, gang, a dark, spooky tunnel..."

SHAGGY
"Dark and spooky? No good ever comes from dark and spooky..."

Dude Shaggy-speak for a cool guy, often said in reference to his best pal Scooby.

E

Eating-machines Scooby and Shaggy are always hungry and will eat pretty much anything. *See* **All-you-can-eat buffet, Scooby Snacks** and **Shaggy Sandwich.**

> "Let's do what we do best, Scooby. Eat."
> SHAGGY

F

> "There's an unidentified freaky object in here..."
> SHAGGY

Freaky objects The world of Scooby-Doo is full of these in the form of ghastly ghouls, spooky spectres and all sorts of creepy creatures (rikes!).

Fred (Full name Fred Jones) Handsome hero with a penchant for solving mysteries and inventing crazy traps to catch ghosts. *See* **Ascot necktie** and **Let's split up**.

G

Gags Scoobs and Shaggy love to laugh and are often found chortling over one of Shaggy's gags.

Ghosts and ghouls
Coolsville is crawling with these, from the phantom Black Knight and the ghoulish Diver to the Ghost Clown and goggle-eyed Zombie.

Glasses Thick-rimmed and square, these are a crucial element of Velma's brainbox look. They're often lost during particularly exciting chases as Velma is left fumbling around on the floor for them. (*See* **Velma**.)

Goofs Shaggy and Scooby-Doo are a fine example of these and are often told to quit 'goofing around'.

H

Haunted houses A typical hang-out for the gang in search of ghosts and ghouls. Creepy castles with spooky butlers, dungeons and winding staircases make for a truly scary experience.

I

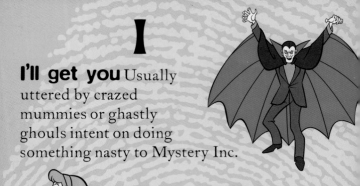

I'll get you Usually
uttered by crazed
mummies or ghastly
ghouls intent on doing
something nasty to Mystery Inc.

J

Jeepers! A favourite phrase
of Daphne's, usually said
when she's in real trouble.
See **Daphne**.

Jinkies! Velma's groovy catchphrase, often exclaimed when she's finally pieced together all the clues and figured out the mystery. *See* **Velma**.

k

Knight The Black Knight was one of the first villains ever encountered by the Scooby-Doo gang. Scooby also loves to dress up as a knight whenever the gang visit a haunted house, just to give Shaggy a bit of a fright (ree-hee-hee!).

L

Let's split up Helpful suggestion often voiced by Fred just as the gang arrive at a spooky house. This is usually the last thing they should do. *See* **Fred**.

"Like, everybody run!"

Like, wow Shaggy's, like, uniquely groovy way of speaking. *See* **Shaggy**.

M

Meddling kids The Scooby-Doo gang are often accused of being this, particularly when they're unmasking a bad guy.

> **"And I would have gotten away with it too if it weren't for you meddling kids..."**

Monsters You name it, Coolsville's got 'em, from Frankenstein and the weirdo Wax Phantom to zombies and the two-million-year-old caveman (relp!).

Mystery Inc. Formal name for the super-sleuthing gang who specialise in solving mysteries and catching spooky bad guys.

Mystery Machine Mystery Inc.'s distinctive and very cool set of wheels. Also serves as a mobile HQ for the gang.

N

Nighttime As ghouls and ghosts tend to surface at the dead of night, the mystery-solving business is strictly an after-hours affair.

"Nothin' to be afraid of, ole' buddy!"

O

On to something Pretty early on, the gang usually find a crucial clue to spur them on in their detective work.

P

Plan Crucial to all detective work, born-leader Fred usually comes up with one of these.

Puppy Power Annoying phrase coined by Scooby-Doo's nephew, Scrappy-Doo, in the mistaken belief he can take on any monster. *See* **Scrappy-Doo**.

> FRED
> **"We need to come up with a plan."**
> SHAGGY
> **"Hiding is our plan."**

Q

Quake When faced with a terrifying situation, Scooby and Shaggy literally tremble with fear, usually followed by one of them jumping into the other's arms.

"We'll need to catch the ghost red-handed just to be sure."

R

Red-handed Central to all mystery-solving is to catch your crook in action. *See* **Bait** and **Trap**.

S

Scooby-Doo (Full name Scoobert) Loveable, canine-coward who can usually be lured into action with a Scooby Snack. Best buddy is Shaggy (Raggy). *See* **Scooby Speak** (in appendix), **Scooby Snack** and **Tail-power**.

Scooby Snacks

Irresistible butterscotch-flavoured treats that Scooby and Shaggy will do just about anything for.

Scrappy-Doo

Scooby-Doo's pain-in-the-butt nephew.
See **Puppy Power**.

FRED
"Do you think you could run faster for a Scooby Snack?"

SHAGGY
"Really, is there anything we won't do for Scooby Snacks?"

Shaggy (Full name Norville Rogers)

Big scaredy-cat who likes nothing more than eating, goofing around and running away from danger. Scooby is a fellow goof and best buddy.
See **Shaggy Sandwich** and **Zoinks!**

Shaggy Sandwich Legendary, multi-decked, super-size sandwich fit for the greediest of cartoon heroes. (*See* **All-you-can-eat-buffet**, **Eating-machines** and **Scoobe Snacks**.)

T

Trap The best way to catch a villain red-handed is to set up one of these, with Scooby and Shaggy as the bait. (*See* **Bait** and **Red-handed**.)

"There's one way to find out... We'll have to set a trap..."

Tail-power Scooby-Doo's tail has a life of its own and usually alerts him to the first sign of trouble by standing up straight. (*See* **Scooby-Doo**.)

Totally Absolutely – Shaggy-style.

U

Unmasking A seminal moment in any Scooby-Doo storyline. (*See* **Meddling Kids** and **Villains**.)

V

Velma (Full name **Velma Dinkley**) Mystery-solving brainbox who firmly believes there is no such thing as ghosts and tries to find a logical solution to every mystery (so long as she hasn't lost her glasses). *See* **Glasses** and **Jinkies!**

Villains Mystery-Inc. has learnt that, behind a spooky mask, anyone can be one of these, from a crusty old lawyer to a trusted bank manager. (*See* **Unmasking**.)

W

Wowee! What the gang say when they find something eerie or are frightened.

X

X-ray specs Part of Mystery Inc.'s impressive arsenal of sleuthing gadgets. Along with night-vision goggles, infra-red glasses and binoculars, these are perfect for tracking down ghosts and secret stashes of Scooby Snacks!

SHAGGY
"We're gonna die!"
DAPHNE
"Think positively."
SHAGGY
"We're gonna die quickly!"

Y

Yikes! Yelled when Scooby and Shaggy are, like, really scared.

Z

Zoinks! Shaggy's all-time favourite word, usually said when he's had the fright of his life. *See* **Shaggy**.

Zombie Often green and goggle-eyed, and accompanied by a cackling witch or two.

"Zoinked-out monster madness!"

Scooby Speak

Scooby-Doo has a unique way of talking, much of which only Shaggy can understand. Examples include:

Raggy Who else but Scooby's best buddy, Shaggy.

Ree-hee-hee! Goofs Scooby and Shaggy share a joke.

Relp! A plea of help when things have got really dicey.

Rikes! *See* **Yikes**.

Rooby-Dooby-Doo! An exclamation of utter happiness.

Rooby Rack *See* **Scooby Snack**.

Rorr-ree An expression of remorse, usually said when Scooby's landed Shaggy in deep doo-doo.

Ruh-roh! Frequently uttered by Scooby when he's terrified.